Ask me another RIDDLE

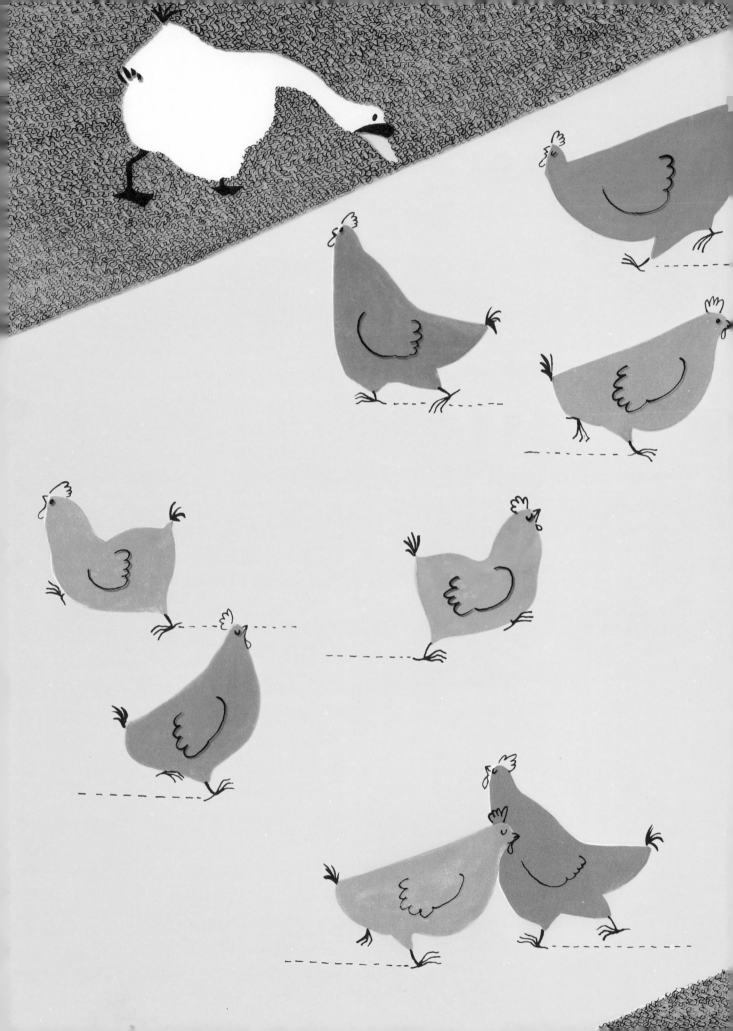

Ask me another
RIDDLE

Compiled by RALPH UNDERWOOD
Pictures by CROSBY BONSALL

ISBN: 0-448-02938-3 (trade edition)   ISBN: 0-448-03228-7 (library edition)

© 1964, by Grosset & Dunlap, Inc.

1975 PRINTING

GROSSET & DUNLAP · Publishers · NEW YORK

What kind of keys
won't open a door?

What always weighs the same,
no matter what size it is?

If you were painting a picture,
what color would you use
for the sun and wind?

What word
becomes shorter
if you add
two letters to it?

Monkeys, turkeys, and donkeys.

A hole.

The sun rose, the wind blue.

Short.

What did the hen say
when she laid a square egg?

A man smashed a clock
and was brought to trial
for killing time.
He was acquitted. Why?

What question can you
never answer "yes" to?

Where was the
Declaration of Independence
signed?

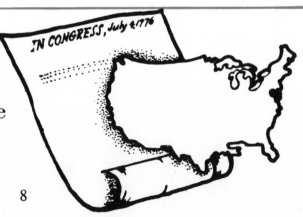

The clock struck first.

"Are you sleeping?"

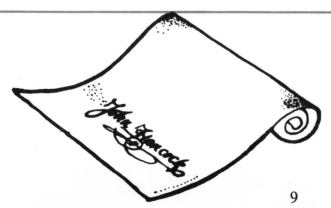

At the bottom.

9

What is black and white and red all over?

What animal does a baby
taking a bath resemble?

Why do weeping willows weep?

What can you swallow that
can also swallow you?

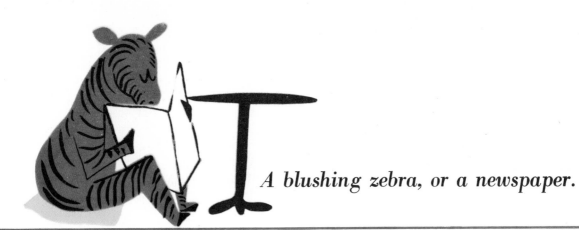

A blushing zebra, or a newspaper.

A little bear.

They are sorry for the pine trees that pine.

Water.

What would you call a sleeping bull?

What kind of driver
never gets a speeding ticket?

What can you hold without touching it?

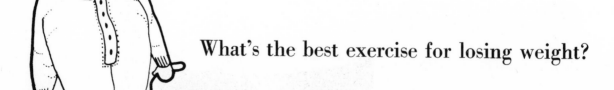

What's the best exercise for losing weight?

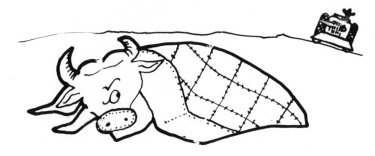

A bulldozer.

A screwdriver.

Your tongue.

Pushing yourself  *away from the table.*

What is the name of a big green house,
That's built around a big white house,
Inside of which is a fine red house,
Full of little brown babies?

Why did the silly billy
tiptoe past the medicine chest?

When is a letter all wet?

What did one chick
say to the other chick
after the hen laid an orange
instead of an egg?

Watermelon.

He didn't want to wake
the sleeping pills.

When it has postage due.

"Look at the orange marmalade!"

What has four eyes?

What did the toothbrush
say to the toothpaste?

What letters are not in the alphabet?

Why is a traffic policeman
the strongest man in the world?

MISSISSIPPI

"*I'm going to give you a squeeze when I meet you on the bridge.*"

The ones in the mailbox.

He can hold up a five-ton truck with one hand.

What is worse than finding a worm in an apple?

What is bad about putting on a shoe?

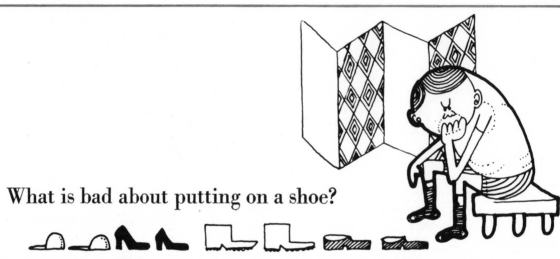

Why are hurricanes named after girls?

Why are knots used to measure distance
on the ocean, instead of miles?

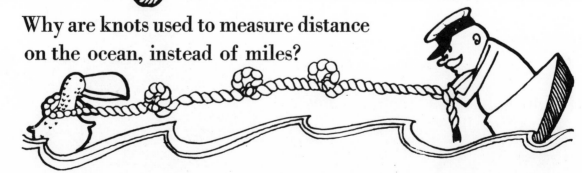

Finding half a worm.

You always put your foot in it.

Because they're not himicanes.

Because of the tide (tied).

 Why are little boys like flannel?

 Who was the greatest actor in history?

 What kind of a cat crawls like a snake?

 When is a dog most likely to enter a house?

They both shrink from washing.

Samson. He brought down the house.

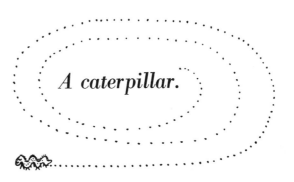

A caterpillar.

When the door is open.

 Why do baby pigs eat so much?

Why didn't the silly billy
ever use toothpaste?

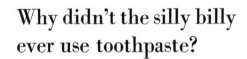

 Why are the measles like a mousetrap?

What did one toe say
to the other toe?

They all want to make hogs of themselves.

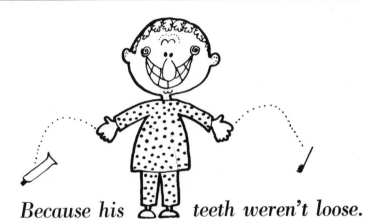

Because his teeth weren't loose.

They are both catching.

"Don't look now, but there's a heel following us."

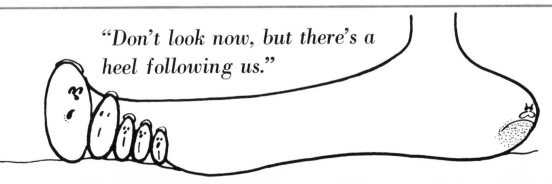

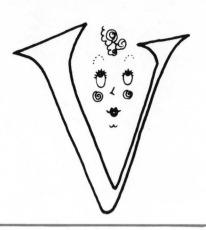

Why is the letter V like a young girl?

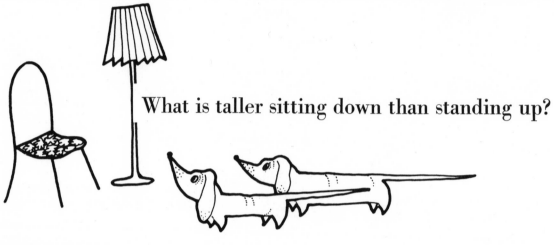

What is taller sitting down than standing up?

What can be heard and caught, but never seen?

When can't a frog croak?

Because
it is
always in love.

 *A dog.*

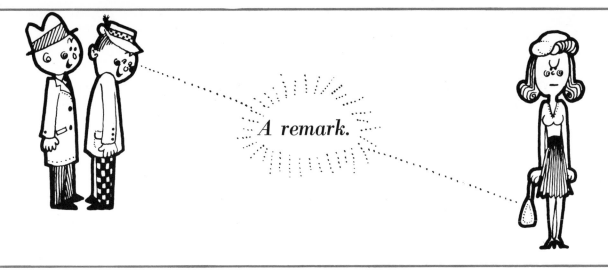 *A remark.*

When he has a man
in his throat.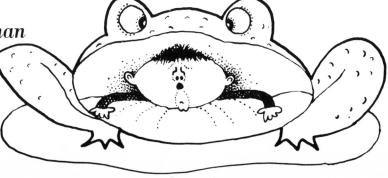

Why is a storm like a baby?

How can you make one pound of shrimp go as far as a hundred pounds of fish?

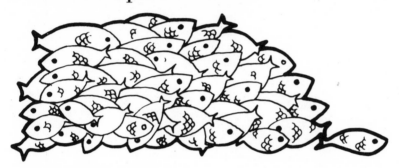

Who has the most people for dinner?

Why is a good President like a good carpenter?

They both start with a squall.

Freeze them both, and
ship them to Chicago.

A cannibal.

They are both fine cabinetmakers.

What does everyone always overlook?

What is often brought to the table,
always cut when it is brought,
yet never eaten?

How can you spell mousetrap with three letters?

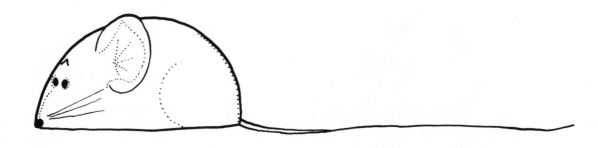

What did the tablecloth
say to the table?

28

His nose.

A deck of cards.

C-A-T.

"Don't move! I've got you covered!"

29

Why did the silly billy take a hammer to bed with him?

Why is the letter A like a flower?

Who can stay single,
even if he marries many women?

What goes through the door,
but never enters
or leaves the house?

He wanted to hit the hay.

Because the B comes after it.

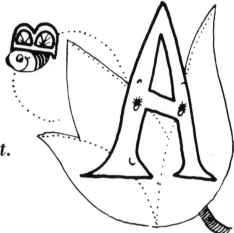

A minister.

A keyhole.

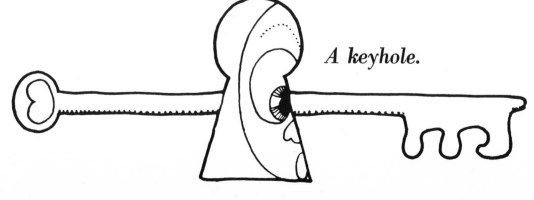

The Chinese man was on his way to the dentist.
What time was it?

What kind of fish can you find in a bird cage?

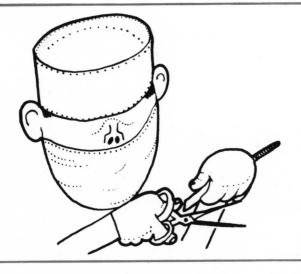

Which state is a physician?

What did the tall chimney
say to the short chimney?

Tooth hurtee!

A perch.

Md.

"You're not big enough to smoke!"

Why is the letter 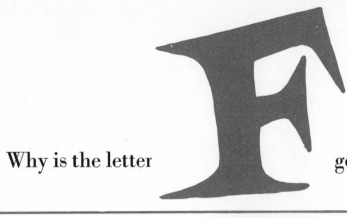 good for planting seeds?

 Why did the silly billy stand in back of the donkey?

What kind of pets make the best music?

Why did the jelly roll?

Because it makes an arm farm.

He thought he would get a kick out of it.

Trumpets.

 It saw the apple turnover.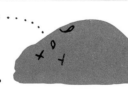

What tree resembles a calendar?

What kind of berries live the longest?

Why does a gardener detest weeds?

What can give you the power
to see through walls?

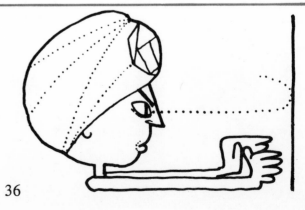

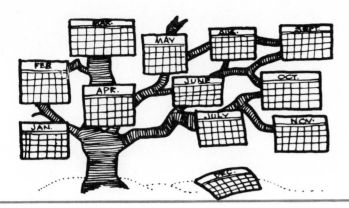

A date tree.

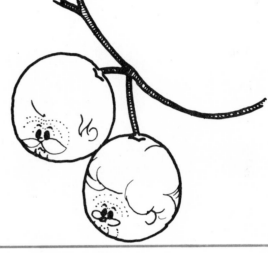

Elderberries.

*Because when you give them an inch,
they take a yard.*

Windows.

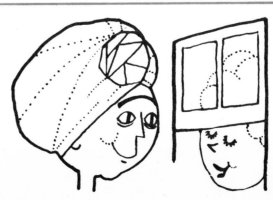

Which is the richest country in the world?

Why is a lame elephant like a student adding six and seven?

Why was the silly billy crying at her own wedding?

Why are dentists such sad men?

Dublin Dublin

Ireland—its capital is always **Dublin Dublin**

Because he puts down three and carries one.

Because she didn't marry the best man.

Because they are always looking down in the mouth.

Why is the letter  like a hot day?

How many big men
have been born
in small towns?

Why is English called the mother tongue?

What kind of suit
is best for a stout man?

Because it is in the
middle of

AUGUST

None—only babies.

Because Father
seldom gets a chance
to use it.

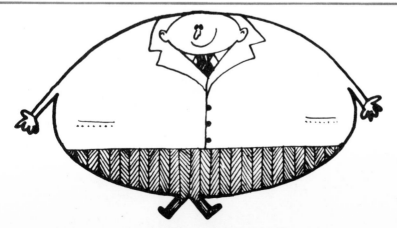

One of broadcloth.

What kind of a stone is a fake?

What three inventions
have helped men
get up the most?

SOUTH

Why do birds fly south in the winter?

Why is the letter H good for a deaf man?

A shamrock.

The airplane, the elevator, and the alarm clock.

 1,802 MI. (as the crow flies)

Because it's too far to walk.

Because it makes an ear hear.

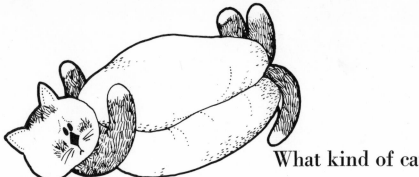

What kind of cat is good to eat?

How many peas are there in a pint?

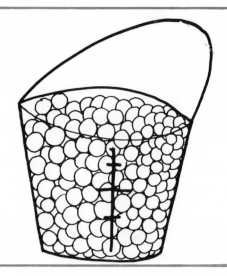

What tree is like a coat?

Why should a doctor
always keep his temper?

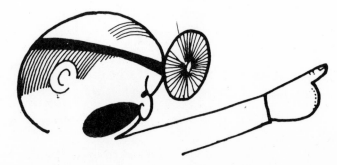

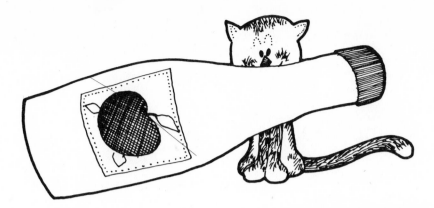

Catsup.

One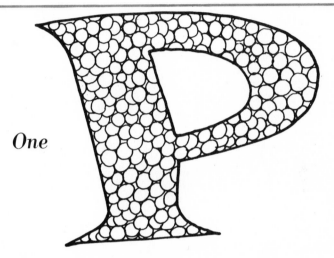

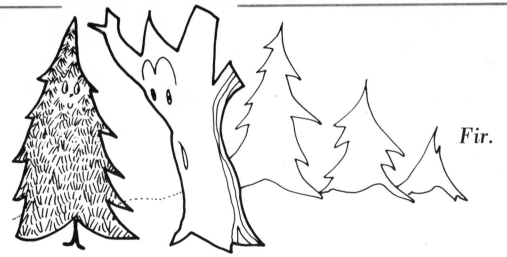

Fir.

He can't afford to lose patients.

Why does the Statue of Liberty stand in New York Harbor?

Why did the silly billy take a cigarette from his pack?

What is the worst kind of range to cook on?

Which state is always ailing?

Because it can't sit down.

He was trying to make it a cigarette lighter.

A mountain range.

What has many teeth, but can't eat?

What should you take when you are run down?

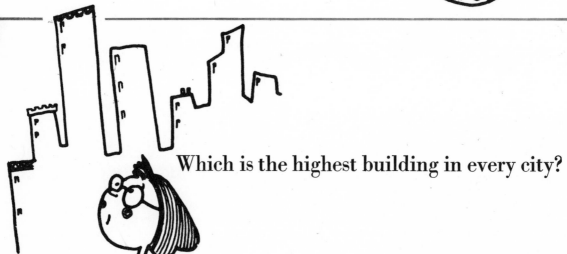

Which is the highest building in every city?

Why did the farmer name one pig "Ink"?

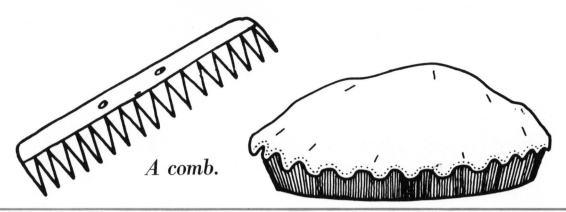

A comb.

The license number of the car that hit you.

The library always has the most stories.

Because he kept running out of the pen.

If you threw a black stone into the Red Sea,
what would happen to it?

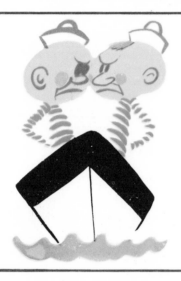

What ship has no captain, but two mates?

When do dachshunds have eight legs?

Why is the letter 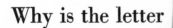 used in steel mills?

It would get wet.

 Courtship.

 *When there are two of them.*

Because it makes  *out of ore.*

What did the mayonnaise say
to the refrigerator?

Which animal is best at spelling?

Why was the silly billy
using a steamroller
on his farm?

For what man does everyone remove his hat?

"Close the door. I'm dressing."

He was trying to raise mashed potatoes.

The barber.

Why is a judge like an Eskimo?

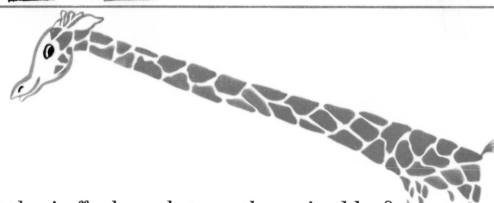

What do giraffes have that no other animal has?

What is the difference between a churchbell and an orange?

What is the last thing you take off when you go to bed?

 They are both connected with just-ice.

 Baby giraffes.

 An orange can be peeled only once.

Your feet from the floor.

55

What kind of cord is full of knots
that cannot be untied?

Why is a policeman like a crack
in a bench?

What is a calf after it's six months old?

If a car has a horn, but no motor
and no wheels, how can it go?

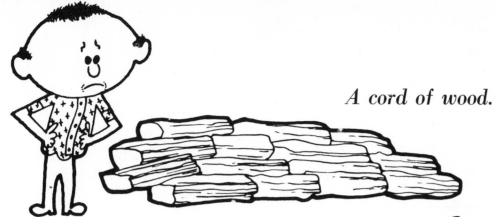

A cord of wood.

They will both pinch you
if you park wrong.

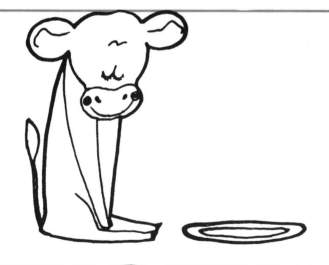

Seven months old.

BEEP! BEEP!

Why did the silly billy
cut a hole in the carpet?

What should an envelope do
when you lick it?

What are most people doing
when it is raining
cats and dogs?

What kind of a bow is impossible to tie?

He wanted to see the floor show.

It should just shut up and say nothing.

Hailing taxicabs.

A rainbow.

If two is company and three is a crowd, what are four and five?

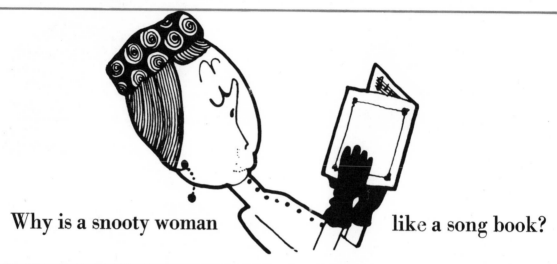

Why is a snooty woman like a song book?

Why did the sofa say that the end table was too emotional?

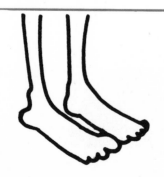

What kind of shoes would you make out of banana skins?

NINE

They are both 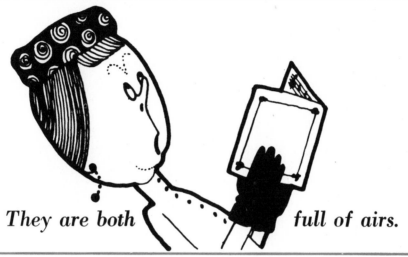 full of airs.

Because it was easily moved.

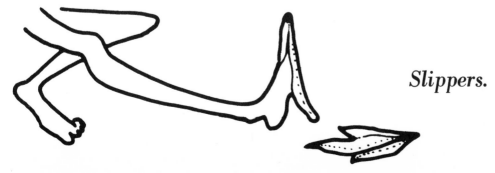 Slippers.

What is all white going up,
but yellow and white
when it comes down?

How did the silly billy get into his house
when the door and the windows were locked
and he had lost his key?

When is a river angry?

Which state is a number?

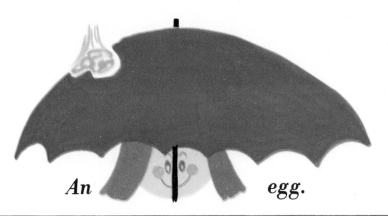

An   egg.

He ran around and around
until he was all in.

When something crosses it.

10

Tenn.

What has one foot at each end, and a third foot in the middle?

If you found an egg in a basket floating in the Hudson River, where would the egg have come from?

What's the difference between a book and a bore?

Why is a heavy snowfall like a good story?

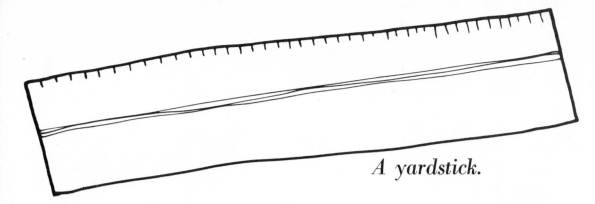

A yardstick.

A hen.

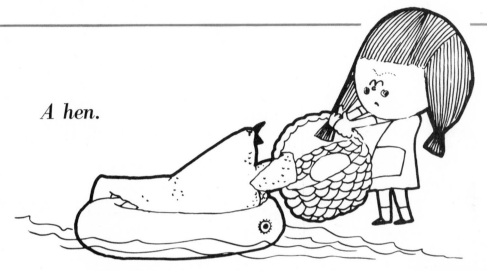

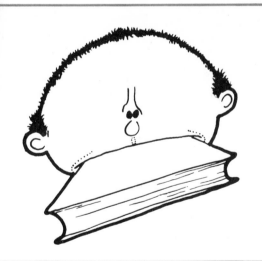

A bore is hard to shut up.

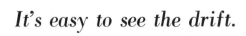

It's easy to see the drift.

Which weighs more,
a full moon or a quarter moon?

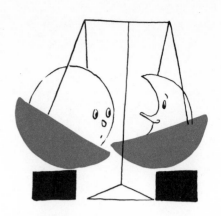

What's the difference
between a dull student
and a fisherman?

Why are fish so well educated?

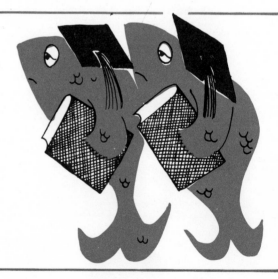

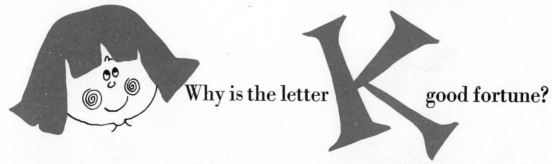

Why is the letter **K** good fortune?

A full moon is lighter.

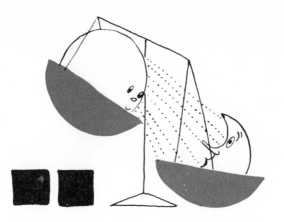

The dull student hates his books.
The fisherman baits his hooks.

You usually find them in schools.

Because it makes Lucy lucky.

What has a head like a cat,
eyes like a cat,
a tail like a cat, but isn't a cat?

What comes right up to the door
but never enters the house?

On what day should you eat the most?

What kind of present is it proper
to kick about?

A kitten.

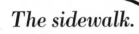

The sidewalk.

Halloween—it's the best for a goblin.

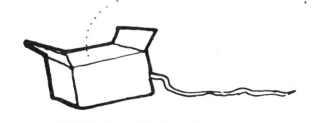

A football.

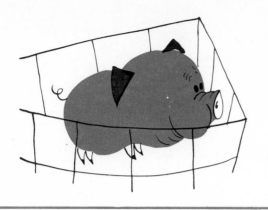

If one pig is in a pen, and another pig is running loose in the farmyard, which one is singing, "Don't fence me in"?

What is the hardest part about learning to ice skate?

Why did the silly billy take a ladder to school?

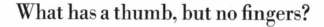

What has a thumb, but no fingers?

Neither one—pigs can't sing.

The ice.

He wanted to go to high school.

A mitten.

Why are horses
very hard to get along with?

Why did the silly billy
jump out of the window?

What always has its heart in its head?

A hippopotamus is sitting on a chair.
What time is it?

They always say "neigh."

He had on his light fall coat.

Lettuce.

Time to get a new chair.

What is the best kind of nut to eat when you have a cold?

How can you always tell when a train has left the station?

Why is a dog in an automobile like a floor covering?

Why is the letter 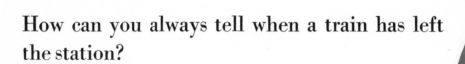 good for runners?

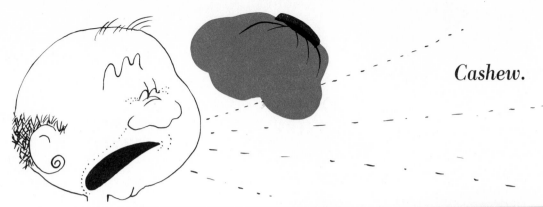

Cashew.

It leaves its tracks behind.

Because it is a car pet.

Because it makes feet fleet.

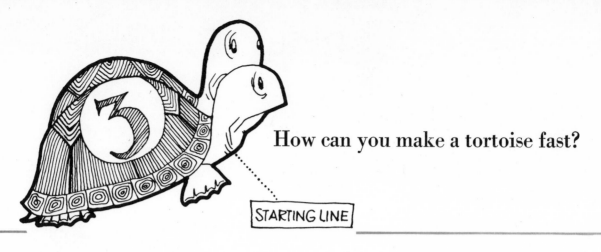

How can you make a tortoise fast?

If cookies cost twenty-six cents a dozen, how many could you buy for a cent and a quarter?

What kind of room is never part of a house?

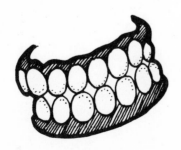

What has a thousand teeth but no mouth?

Take his food away.

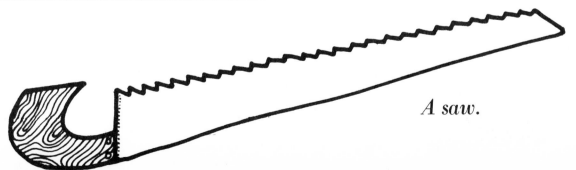

Twelve.

A mushroom.

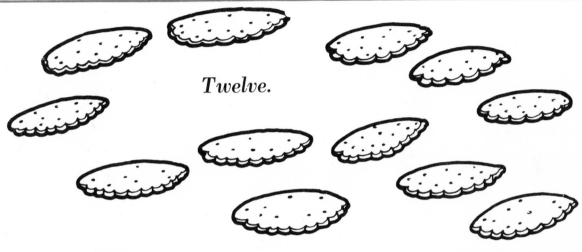

A saw.

Which state is a boat?

How can you find a cheater out?

Where did the silly billy try to find the English Channel?

Peter Piper picked a peck of pickled peppers. Can you spell that without using any P?

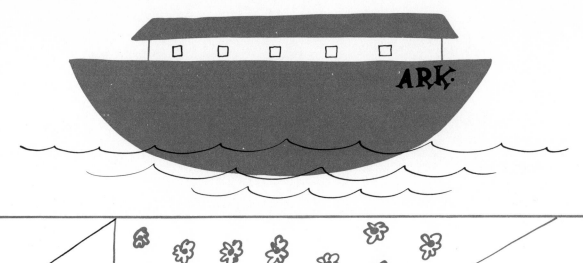

Go to his house when he's not there.

On his TV set.

How would one minister
call another minister
long distance?

What did the beaver say to the tree?

Three men fell out of a boat,
but only two got their hair wet. Why?

What was the name of the first satellite to
orbit the earth?

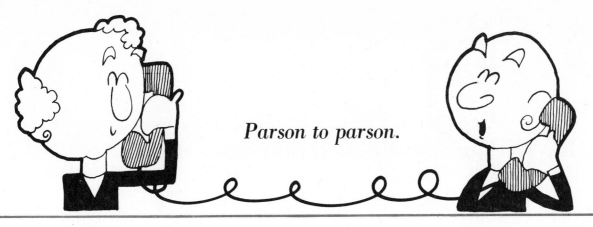

Parson to parson.

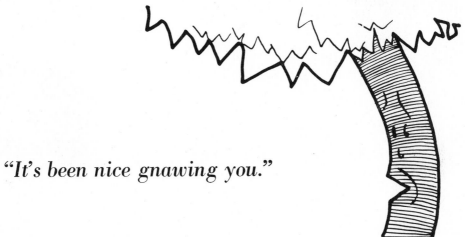

"It's been nice gnawing you."

The third one was bald.

The moon.

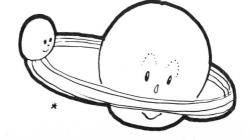

Why does a dog turn around several times before he lies down?

What is as light as air,
yet the strongest man
can't hold it for ten minutes?

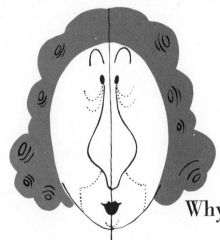

Why is your nose in the middle of your face?

What is the best thing
to put in a meatloaf?

 Because one good turn deserves another.

 His breath.

Because it's the scenter.

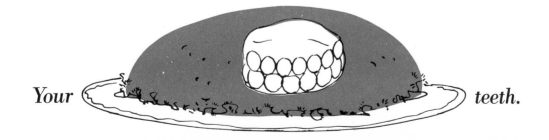 Your teeth.

Why can't a bride keep a secret?

Why is a vacation in the mountains
more expensive
than one at the seashore?

How would you clean your clothes if you were
on a desert island?

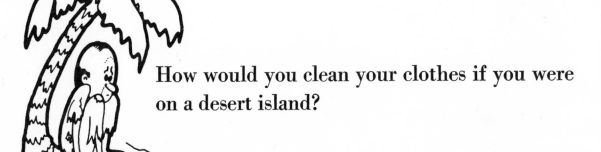

How many ants will make a landlord happy?

Because someone always gives her away.

Because everything is higher in the mountains.

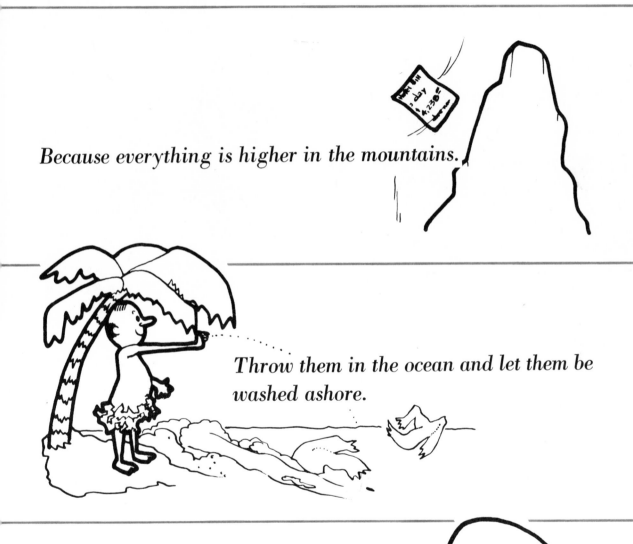

Throw them in the ocean and let them be washed ashore.

Ten ants.

Why was the taxicab driver's business bad?

Why did the silly billy call the elevator operator "Daddy"?

How can you make sure there are no baby chicks in the eggs you buy?

Why is it easier to clean a mirror than a window?

He drove away all of his customers.

Because he had brought him up.

Buy duck eggs.

Because a mirror has only one side.

How far can an explorer go into a jungle?

Where can you always find money?

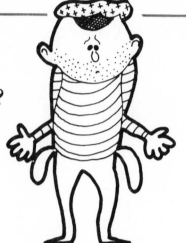

Why didn't the silly billy
ever return books
that he borrowed?

What always goes to sleep with shoes on?

Halfway. Any farther than that and he will be coming out.

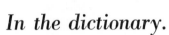
In the dictionary.

He was a bookkeeper.

A horse.

Ten wild geese were perched on a fence.
A hunter shot one. How many were left?

Why is a cloud like a jockey?

What is black on the inside,
white on the outside,
and hot?

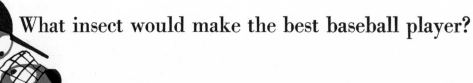
What insect would make the best baseball player?

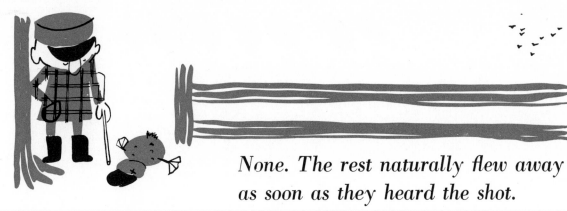

None. The rest naturally flew away as soon as they heard the shot.

They both hold the rains.

A wolf in sheep's clothing.

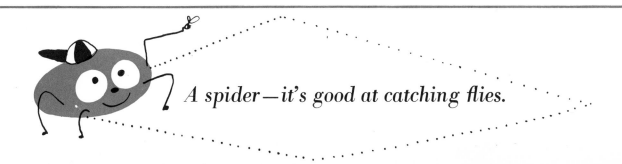

A spider—it's good at catching flies.

Why is a baby like an old car?

What do they call baby cats in Siam?

Who are the best letter writers?

What can you break with your voice?

They both have a rattle.

Kittens.

Fishermen—
they are always dropping a line.

SILENCE

LIBRARIAN

Why is a pig
stuck halfway over a fence
like a coin?

Why did the silly bald man throw his keys away?

Why do you always find
what you are looking for
in the last place you look?

Why is a worm in a cornfield
like a silly remark?

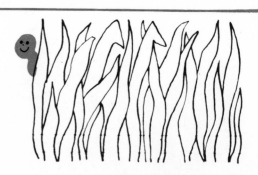

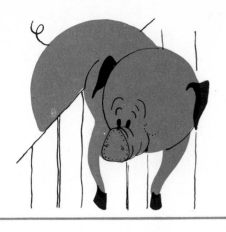

Because his head is on one side
and his tail on the other.

Because he had lost his locks.

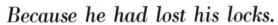

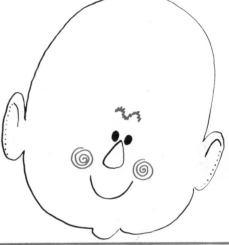

Because once you find it, you stop looking.

They both go in one ear
and out the other.

If you were locked in a room
with nothing in it
but a bed and a calendar,
how could you eat and drink?

How much of a doughnut
should you eat?

How can you divide four apples
among five people equally?

What word
do you always pronounce wrong?

You could drink from the springs in the bed and eat the dates from the calendar.

The (w)hole thing.

Make applesauce.

First we see a big red mill;
By the mill there is a walk;
At the end of the walk there is a key.
What is it?

When should you go to bed?

What tree is like a pet?

What is made longer by being cut?

Milwaukee

When your bed won't come to you.

Dogwood.

A ditch.

What's in the church, but not in the steeple;
The minister has it, but not the people?

What's the best way
to get down from an elephant?

What kind of coat can be put on wet?

How can you make a baby buggy?

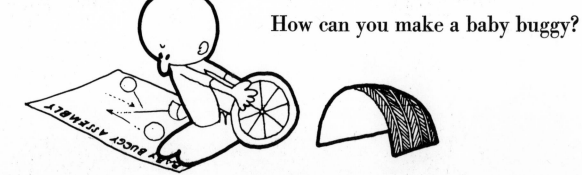

The letter R.

You don't get down from an elephant—
you get down from a goose.

A coat of paint.

Tickle his toes.

Why was one strawberry mad at the other strawberry?

 Why was the mother flea crying?

What should you always do in haste?

 Why did the silly billy
shoo the chickens out of the yard?

Because he felt that he had got him in the jam.

Because her children had gone to the dogs.

Hurry.

Because they were using "fowl" language

What bet can never be won?

What dress does every girl have that she never wears?

What question must you always answer "no" to?

What did the ram say to his sweetheart?

the alphabet

Her address.

What does N-O spell?

"I love ewe."

How much land is the same
as a tooth with a cavity?

What animal was in worse pain than the giraffe
who had a sore throat?

It's red and yellow, blue and green;
The king can't catch it, nor can the queen.
What is this thing that's so hard to get?
Riddle me this and you win a bet.

What time of the year is it when a cat
is about to pounce on a mouse?

An acre.

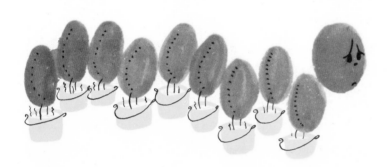

The centipede who had bunions.

A rainbow.

Why is a party
like a tennis game?

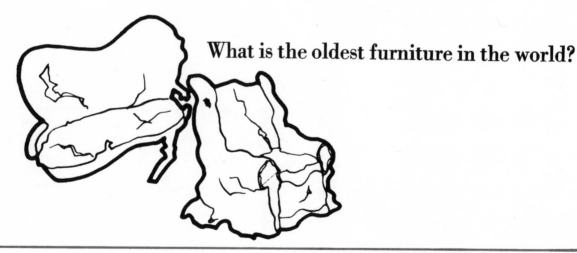

Lying there in the yard so neat
Was something very good to eat;
It had neither flesh nor bone,
But in twenty-one days it walks alone.
What is it?

What is the oldest furniture in the world?

Why is your heart like a policeman?

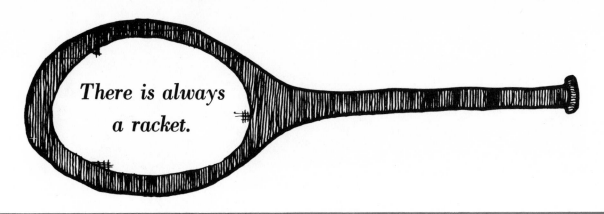

There is always a racket.

An egg.

$2 \times 2 = 4$
$2 \times 3 = 6$
$2 \times 4 = 8$
$2 \times 5 = $ ~~11~~ ~~9~~
~~27~~ ~~14~~ ~~13~~

The arithmetic tables.

$$
\begin{array}{r}
2\\
2\\
2\\
2\\
+\,2\\
\hline
10
\end{array}
$$

It has a regular beat.

Why did the dog try to bite his tail?

Why did the silly billy
push his bed into the fireplace?

What book has the most stirring chapters?

What white bird
glides through the air,
and lights on every tree
that's there?

He was trying to make ends meet.

He wanted to sleep like a log.

A cook book.

Snow.

111

What do you make lower
when you put a head on it?

What is the dearest food?

Why is a circus like a delicatessen?

What is full of holes,
yet can hold water?

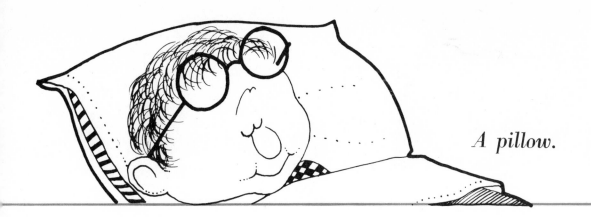

A pillow.

Venison.

In a circus you can see
a man-eating tiger.
In a delicatessen you can see
a man eating. herring.

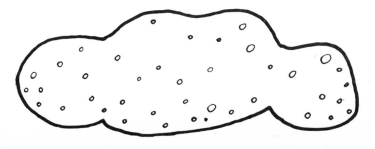

A sponge.

Which is faster,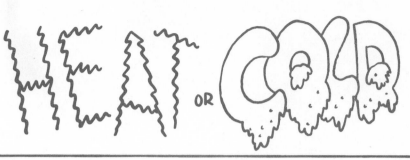

 If there were only three girls left in the whole world, what would they talk about?

Why did Adam take a bite out of the apple?

What was the caterpillar's New Year's resolution?

Heat—you can catch cold.

Two of them would talk about
the other one.

He didn't have  a knife or a fork.

To turn over a new leaf.

Why is the letter U like a rabbit's foot?

When is the only time
that you should lose your temper?

Why don't veterinarians
like to treat pigs?

Take care of me and I'm everyone;
Drop me and I'm no one.
Who am I?

Because it's always in  LUCK

 When it is bad.

Because they can only be cured
after they die.

 A mirror.

What kind of fish sings the best?

What looks like a box, smells like a cigar, and flies?

Why did the silly billy take a mosquito
to Hollywood?

Where can you find water
That never rained or run;
Or a nice quick-drying towel,
That was not wove nor spun?

A bass.

A flying cigar box.

He wanted it to pass a screen test.

Presenting Mickey Mosquito

dew and Sun

What can hold up a train?

How can you always be sure of starting a fire
with two sticks?

What's the difference
between a skunk
and bottle of milk?

What kind of cat
is not afraid of the water?

Bandits.

Make one of them a match.

If you don't know,
I'd never send you
to buy a bottle of milk.

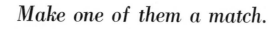

A catfish.

What never gets hurt when it falls?

What does a girl look for very often,
but hopes not to find?

Where was Simple Simon
when the lights went out?

Which state is a father?

DELIVERY ROOM

Snow.

A run in her stocking.

In the dark.

PA.

 What has everyone seen,
but no one will ever see it again?

 When is the best time to buy a pig?

  What must you do if the baby swallows a pencil?

What is it that no man wants,
yet no man wants to lose it?

yesterday

When you have a sty in your eye.

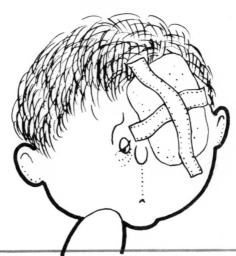

Use a pen.

A bald head.

Where is the largest diamond
in New York City kept?

If your unc'e's sister isn't your aunt,
what is she to you?

Why did the silly billy
put the automobile wheel in his bed?

What is the difference between
a running girl and a running dog?

In the Yankee Stadium.

Your mother.

Because it was tired.

One wears a skirt, the other pants.

127

Which is the left side of an apple pie?

What comes out when you use
a slug in a soda machine
in the movies?

What does an artist like to draw best?

Which member
of a baseball team
wears the
largest hat?

The part that's not eaten.

The manager.

His salary.

The one with the largest head.

What did the porcupine say
when he bumped into
the cactus plant?

Why are some girls like a salad?

Why did Robin Hood
steal from the rich?

What bus crossed the ocean?

"Excuse me, darling!"

Because they need a lot of dressing.

Because poor people
have no money.

COLUMBUS

What is the difference between a counterfeit five dollar bill and an angry rabbit?

What is the difference between a dressmaker and a farmer?

How can you save falling hair?

What works better when it has something in its eye?

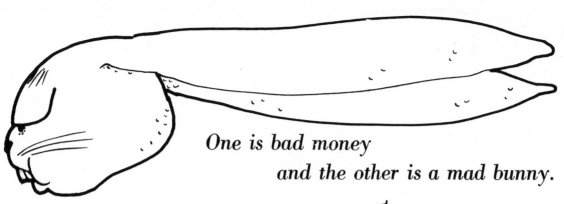

One is bad money
  and the other is a mad bunny.

She sews what she gathers.
He gathers what he sows.

Put it in a cigar box.

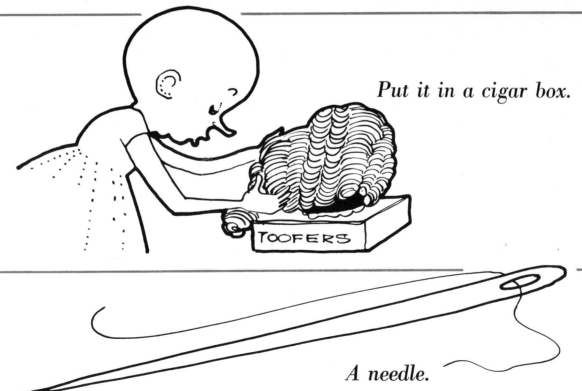

TOOFERS

A needle.

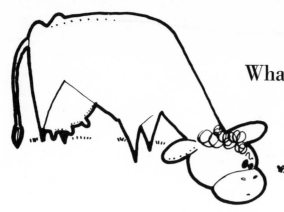

What's the difference between a cow and a flea?

What kind of man has to shave more than three times a day?

Why wouldn't the silly billy put a dime in the telephone?

 What can't be beaten?

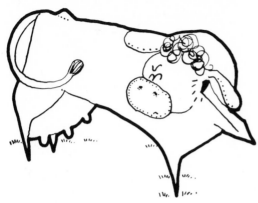

A cow can have fleas,
but a flea can't have cows.

A barber.

He believed in free speech.

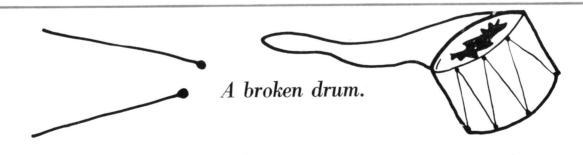

A broken drum.

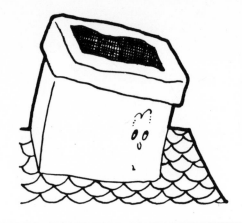

What will go up a chimney down,
but won't go down a chimney up?

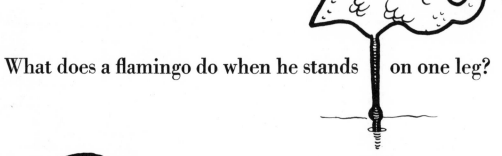

What does a flamingo do when he stands on one leg?

How can you use old letters for clothing?

What's the difference between
a copper penny and a silver quarter?

An umbrella.

He holds up the other one.

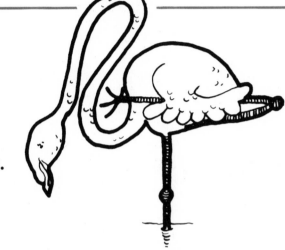

Make yourself a suit of mail
like the knights of old.

Twenty-four cents.

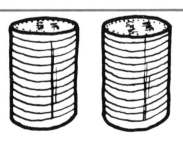

How can you write a letter
that will bring tears to the eyes
of the person it is sent to?

How can a man's net income
be bigger than his gross?

What would be the best dish
to serve at a
sewing circle luncheon?

What is a sure way
to keep milk from getting sour?

Write it on onionskin.

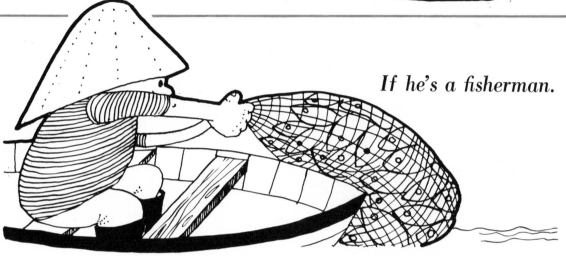

If he's a fisherman.

Round steak.

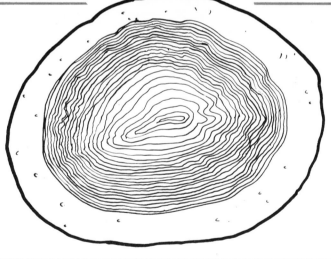

Leave it in the cow.

Why is the center of a tree like a dog's tail?

What is the most important thing
for a teacher to know?

How can you make a skirt last?

What is the longest word
in the English language?

Because it's the part farthest from the bark.

More than her students.

Make the blouse first.

SMILES —there's a mile between two s's.

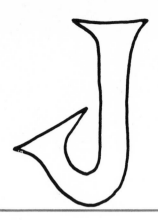

Why is the letter J like a nose?

When is it considered proper etiquette
to serve milk in a saucer?

Why did the silly billy
buy two ducks and a cow?

What day is best for making fish cakes?

Because it is next to eye.

When feeding the cat.

Because he wanted
quackers and milk.

Fry-day.

What state is round at the ends
and high in the middle?

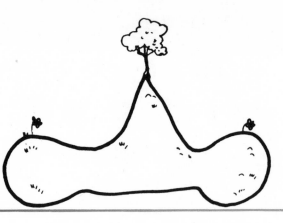

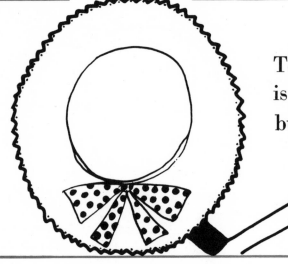

Tell me, please, what it is that
is over your head,
but under your hat?

What is a sure way
      to live to be a hundred years old?

A "C" and an "L" went up to a tree
to make a fine garment
to warm you and me.
What is it?

ohio

Hair.

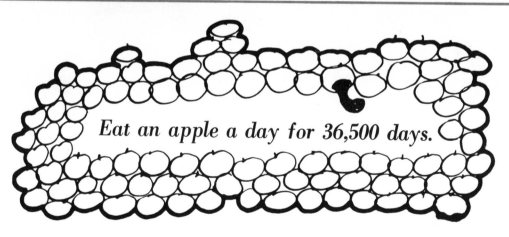

Eat an apple a day for 36,500 days.

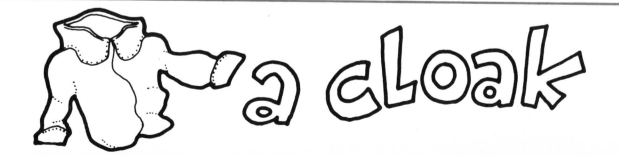

a cloak

Why can't a nose ever be twelve inches long?

When should you feed tiger's milk to a baby?

What kind of beans do children like to eat the most?

Who in the zoo steps on each crack,
And walks away with the world on his back?

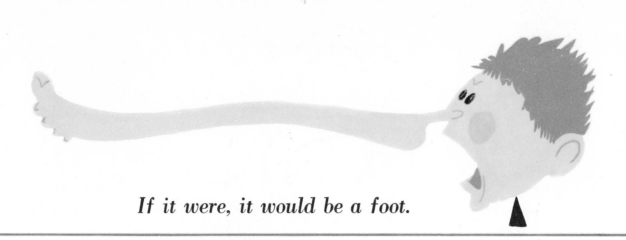

If it were, it would be a foot.

When it's a baby tiger.

Jelly beans

The turtle.

When is the letter  noble?

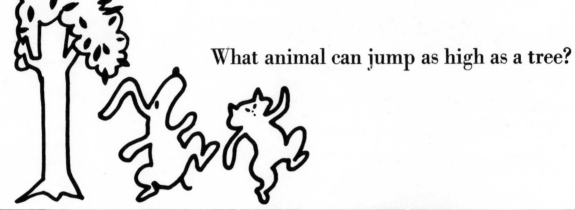 What animal can jump as high as a tree?

 Why didn't the silly billy shoo the flies?

 What musical instrument never tells the truth?

When it is a duchess.

Any animal—trees can't jump.

He wanted them to stay barefoot.

A lyre.

What kind of paper makes the best kites?

How can a man
keep one jump ahead of his wife?

A famous woman movie star
was born in 1919.
How old is she now?

Why does a chicken cross the road?

Flypaper.

By playing checkers with her.

Twenty-nine.

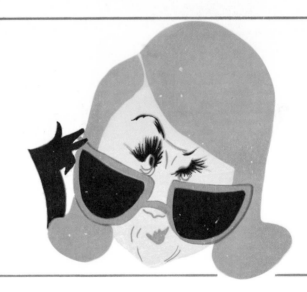

To get to the other side.

What can you put in a can
that will make it weigh less?

Why are giraffes easy to feed?

On what day
do women talk the least?

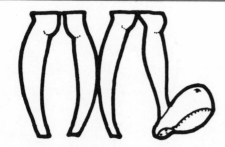

What has four legs, but only one foot?

A hole.

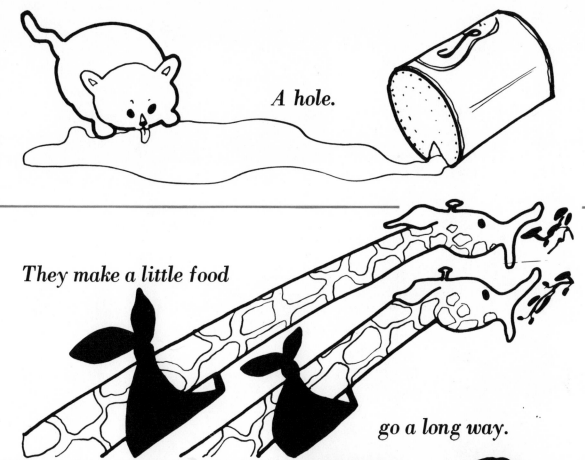

They make a little food

go a long way.

*December twenty-first—
it's the shortest day
of the year.*

A bed.

Where should a dog go if he loses his tail?

Why did the silly exterminator wear ear plugs?

Why are there mirrors on slot machines?

What time is it when the clock strikes thirteen?

To a retail store.

He couldn't stand to hear
a moth bawl.

So you can see how angry you look
when the candy doesn't come out.

Time to fix the clock.

Why is the letter D like a bad boy?

What is a sure way to
double your money?

What kind of a cat
could you find in a library?

I can run and I can whistle;
But I cannot walk or talk.
What am I?

Because it makes Ma mad.

Fold it.

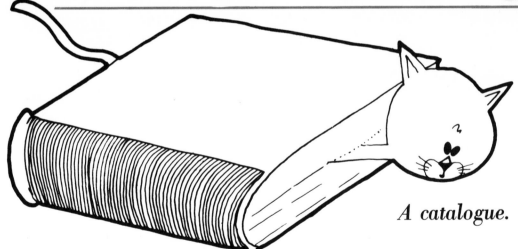

A catalogue.

A railroad locomotive.

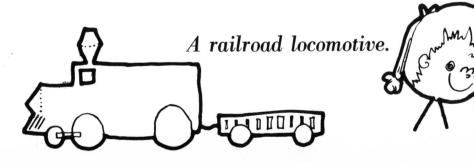

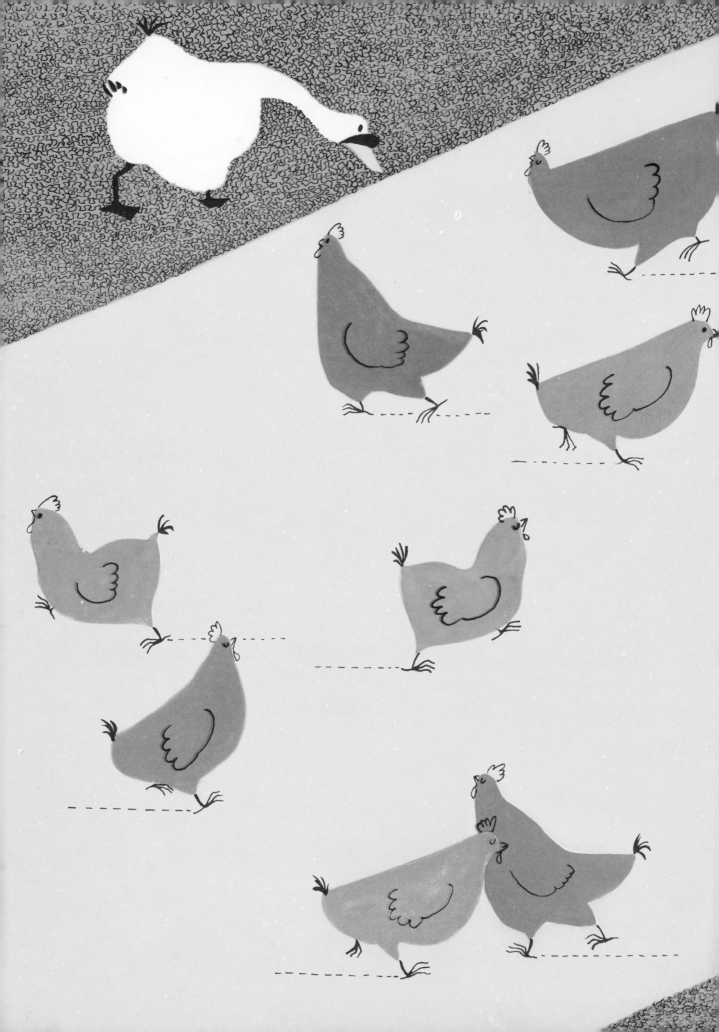